THIS BOOK IS ABOUT

_____

PREPARED, WITH LOVE, BY

_____

Other books in this series:
My Best Recipes
Our Baby's Record Book
Golf Score Book

Other books by Exley:
Household Record Book
Guest Book

Published simultaneously in 1993 by
Exley Publications in Great Britain,
and Exley Giftbooks in the USA.

Edited and pictures selected by Helen Exley.
Designed by Pinpoint Design.
Picture research by P. A. Goldberg and J. M. Clift, Image Select,
London.
Typeset by Delta, Watford.
Printed and bound in Spain by Graficas Reunidas S.A., Madrid.

Exley Publications Ltd, 16 Chalk Hill, Watford,
Herts WD1 4BN, United Kingdom.

Exley Giftbooks, 359 East Main Street, Suite 3D, Mt. Kisco,
NY 10549, USA.

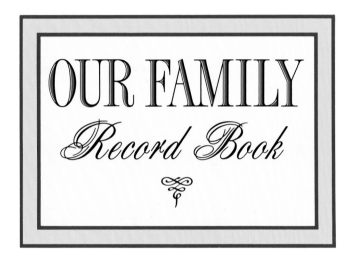

OUR FAMILY
Record Book

EDITED BY
HELEN EXLEY

EXLEY
MT. KISCO, NEW YORK • WATFORD, UK

INTRODUCTION

Most people love to know about their family's roots. This journal provides a framework in which you can tell your family's history. It enables you to capture those special family moments which are so precious: the celebrations and shared joys of a growing family.

Make this book as unique as your own family by using lots of photographs. Encourage everyone to contribute – be it with a best-loved poem or the remembered details of a special occasion.

By filling in the family tree and ensuring that grandparents and other relatives record their own personal memories, you will be preserving your family's history not just for your own children, but for their children too.

HELEN EXLEY

CONTENTS

FILL IN YOUR OWN HEADINGS FOR THE FOLLOWING PAGES. USE THEM FOR EXTRA FAMILY STORIES OR IMPORTANT FAMILY EVENTS.

GREAT GREAT GRANDPARENTS

GREAT GRANDPARENTS   GREAT GRANDPARENTS

GREAT AUNTS AND UNCLES   GREAT AUNTS AND UNCLES

GRANDMOTHER   GRANDFATHER

AUNTS AND UNCLES

MOTHER

BROTHERS AND SISTERS

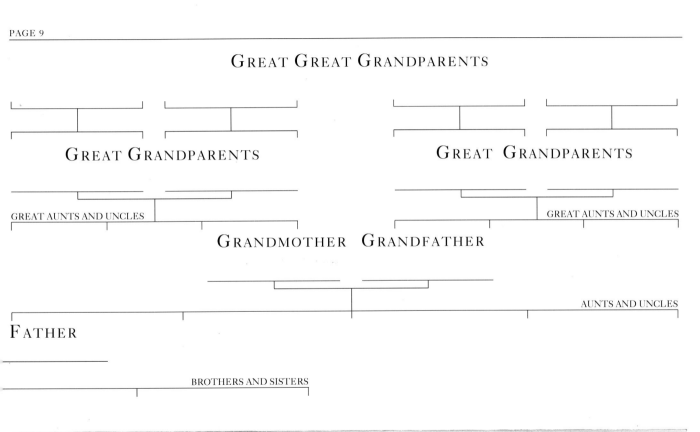

GREAT GREAT GRANDPARENTS

GREAT GRANDPARENTS

GREAT GRANDPARENTS

GREAT AUNTS AND UNCLES

GREAT AUNTS AND UNCLES

GRANDMOTHER GRANDFATHER

AUNTS AND UNCLES

FATHER

BROTHERS AND SISTERS

OUR FAMILY HISTORY

IMPORTANT DATES AND PAST EVENTS

WORLD EVENTS THAT AFFECTED OUR FAMILY

OUR FAMILY NOW

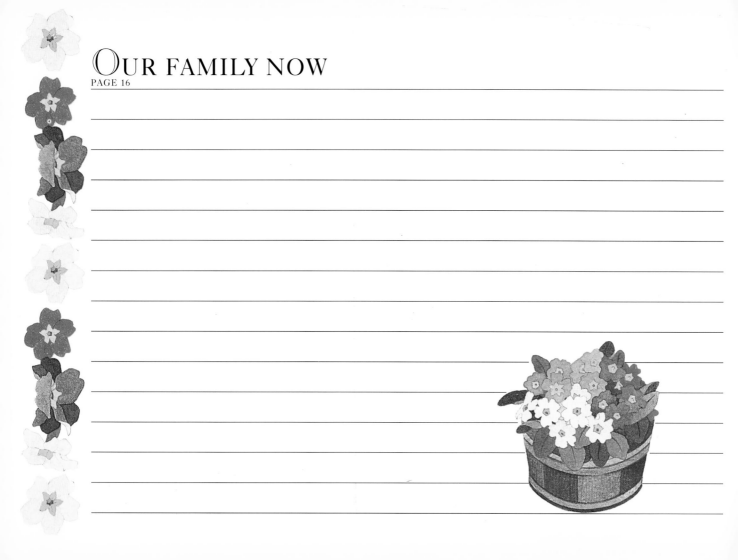

OUR FAMILY'S OCCUPATIONS

OUR INDIVIDUAL AMBITIONS

FAMILY ACHIEVEMENTS

FAMILY CHARACTERISTICS

HAIR

EYES

HEIGHT

OTHER

FAMILY TRADITIONS

TREASURED POSSESSIONS

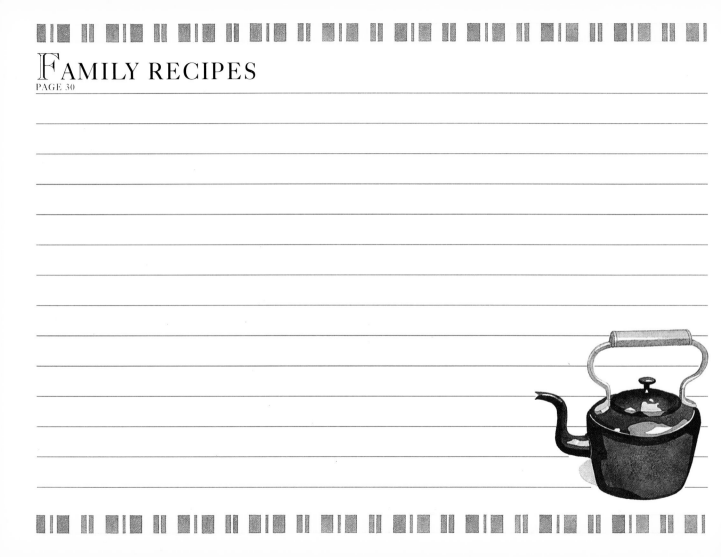

FAMILY RECIPES

BEST-LOVED FAMILY SONGS ETC.

FAMILY SONGS

FAMILY SAYINGS

FAMILY EXPRESSIONS

FAMILY POEMS

SAD TIMES

SPECIAL RELATIVES
PAGE 37

BEST-LOVED FAMILY FRIENDS

SPECIAL TALENTS

ART

MUSIC

DANCE

SPORT

OTHER

SOME HAPPY MEMORIES

IMPORTANT DAYS, OUTINGS, CELEBRATIONS

PAGE 45

BEST-LOVED BOOKS ETC.

BOOKS

MUSIC

FOOD

OTHER

MORE BEST-LOVED ...
PAGE 48

_____

_____

_____

_____

_____

_____

_____

_____

_____

_____

_____

PAGE 49

FUNNIEST MEMORIES

MEMORIES OF KIND ACTIONS

MEMENTOES AND MEMORABILIA

Personal beliefs

Best-loved quotations

OUR PERSONAL WISHES FOR THE FUTURE

OUR INDIVIDUAL LIKES AND DISLIKES

PAGE 65

MOTHER'S STORY

PAGE 66

FATHER'S STORY

PAGE 69

GRANDFATHER'S STORY

GRANDMOTHER'S STORY

GRANDFATHER'S STORY

PAGE 72

GRANDMOTHER'S STORY

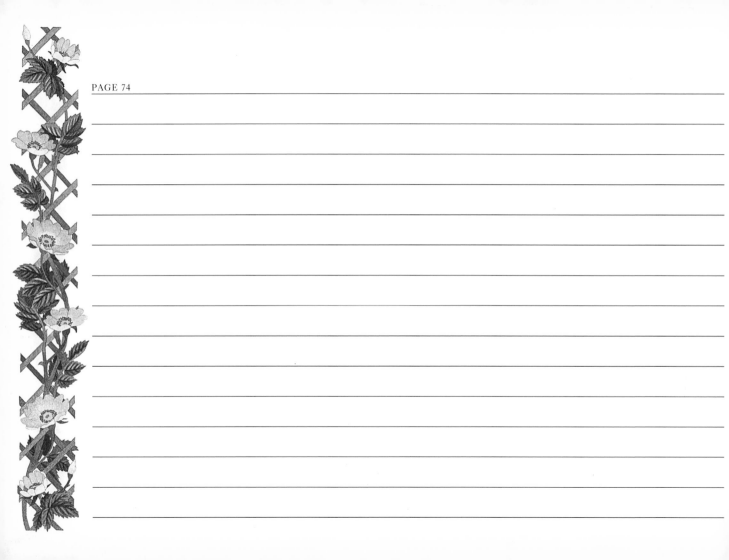

PAGE 74

PAGE 78

PAGE 82

PAGE 86